Wonder Why, Wonder How

Stories that Spark Imagination

by

Chirali Bhandari

Illustrated by Suzena Samuel

DORRANCE
PUBLISHING CO
EST. 1920
PITTSBURGH, PENNSYLVANIA 15238

Dorrance Publishing Co
585 Alpha Drive
Suite 103
Pittsburgh, PA 15238
Visit our website at www.dorrancebookstore.com

ISBN: 978-1-6376-4223-8
eISBN: 978-1-6376-4851-3

For Dada

For Mumma Papu

For Neel

The
Moon
Show

It was nighttime,
and up so high
crescent moon was shining
in the sky.

The moon was out
on his regular round:
smiling at the earth
and everything to be found.

He hovered over a forest
and shone upon the trees
when a sleepy baby plant
looked up for the first time, to see.

'Oh, my dear Moon,
what happened to you?
Why are you so thin?
Where is the rest of you?

Did you lose the rest while getting here?
Or did someone steal it? Oh, no! Oh, dear!
I always thought that the moon was round!
Is the rest of you, nowhere to be found?'

Said the moon, 'Oh, little sapling, don't worry this way!
The rest of me is just hidden away.
Every time I am out during the night,
I change shapes on my flight.

'I go from full to none at all,
then back to full just like a ball
These are moon's phases, the different shapes of me;
the part that gets light is what your eyes see.'

'Wow! That is so interesting,
thank you for letting me know,
It seems like you have
your very own moon show!

As I grow bigger,
and taller over time,
I'll keep an eye out for you
and all your shapes so fine.

'Thank you, dear moon,
for shining bright and high!
It looks beautiful when
you are up in the sky.'

The Very
Colorful Butterfly

There was once a caterpillar
so tiny and so white
he ate leaves during the day
and slept through the night.

There were so many things to eat,
so many new foods to try
but he was afraid of anything new,
so, he only ate what fell nearby.

One day a blueberry fell close to him
and finally, he did try.
Lo and behold! something changed!
His tail turned dark blue! Oh, my!

The white and blue caterpillar
then found a mango
this time it was even more fun
for he now donned a little blue,
and a little yellow.

The blue and yellow slowly mixed
to form a beautiful green,
He was becoming quite the creature!
What happened next, is to be seen.

With blue and green, and yellow
now added to the white,
he now wanted a strawberry
for a color palette so bright!

Once he ate, the red mixed with yellow
to form orange in between
He thought this was most unique!
To add more colors, he was now keen.

He found a bunch of purple grapes
that he ate all in a gulp!
And what color do you think was added?
Of course, it was purple from the pulp!

Happy and content now
he slept in his cocoon:
many a day passed by
and so did many a moon.

One fine day, when he woke up and looked in the pond nearby,
he didn't recognize himself for now, he was a colorful butterfly!

All the healthy eating and all the colors so fine
made him big and strong, and made him look divine.

I am glad I tried the new, he thought. This has been so much fun!
Then he flew to find flowers; his butterfly life had just begun!

From one flower to another, then to the next, he would fly
spreading his wings, and afraid no more,
he was the most cheerful, colorful butterfly.

I Want
the Moon!

It was the dark of the night
there flowed a gentle breeze
it was not too hot, nor too cold
and leaves murmured on the trees.

The moon shone bright
high up in the sky
as a little cub and Mother
went strolling by.

The cub looked up
and saw the moon;
'I want the white ball!' he said,
'please bring it to me soon.

'I wonder who put it there
out of my reach, so high
Mother, please get it for me
from the sky.'

'Oh, my dear, my sweet baby,
it is the moon, not a ball;
it cannot be brought on earth,
it shines not for one, but for all.'

The cub was sad.
Mother knew not what to do
until they came upon a lake
and the cub shouted, 'Woo hoo!'

'Look! There it is, Mother,
it has come down for me,
look in the water
do you see, do you see?'

Off he ran to the shore
to touch the moon with his paw
only to be completely enchanted
by what he next saw!

He looked at the reflection in water,
all white and perfectly round,
what more could the cub want?
His treasure had been found!

He jumped into the lake
splashing water everywhere.
As the moon appeared to play,
happy squeals filled the air.

Gentle waves came and went...
the cub was jumping with joy
Mother thought to herself,
'You did get your moon! Oh, boy!'

The joy of being innocent,
the joy of being a child:
never stop believing
let the dreams run wild.

You just never know
what may come to you soon,
you may find your own treasures
like the cub found his moon.

Planet Song

Knowing about planets
is interesting, and lots of fun!
All eight are very different
although all orbit around the Sun.

The first one is Mercury
it is closest to the Sun
so very hot, and so very cold
it is also the smallest one.

Next comes Venus
which is the hottest of all,
bright like a star in the night sky
it is also the shiniest of them all.

Far away, at number seven,
is Uranus that appears green
made of mainly three types of gases.
With a telescope it can be seen.

The farthest amongst all eight
is Neptune; its color is a beautiful blue
made of gas, just like Uranus,
it is the coldest one, too.

Are we done with the planet names?
I think so, let's see:
I counted eight, but let me state
a science fact that is a bit funny.

You see, we also have Pluto
the ninth planet it used to be
when the scientists looked closer
a dwarf planet it turned out to be!

Though it is no longer a planet
it does go around the Sun
planet or dwarf, full or half,
learning about space is so much fun!

Many billions of galaxies
with planets and stars around
filled with wonder is the sky;
there is so much yet to be found!

The Little Cloud
with a Big Heart

A little white, fluffy cloud
sailed smoothly in the sky,
changing shapes as it pleased
matching what it saw nearby.

When it saw an airplane
it made itself look like one
it didn't sail as fast, though
as there were no passengers within.

It then turned into a train,
chugging along happy and slow
and then into a tree, a bird, a hat,
a shoe, a ball, a toy and snow.

'Oh, what a fun day!' thought the cloud,
'so far, it has been!'
Until it came across a tiny plant,
the tiniest it had ever seen.

It sprung from the seed and soil
and looked thirsty and dry
'You need some water,' the cloud said.
'To help you, I shall try.'

It squeezed itself tight,
really, really, really tight!
But it was out of water!
Oh, no! What a sad sight!

'Hang on, little one,' the cloud said,
'Don't you let go!
I promise I will be back
with water in my tow.'

It then sailed across the sky
where other big clouds were
'Please come with me, quick!
We need to help a tiny plant, come here!'

All the cloud friends got together
and made one giant cloud
they sailed across the sky once again
where the little plant was to be found.

The big cloud showered gently
spraying water where it was dry
the thirsty sapling gulped, and said,
'So nice of you to come by.'

'Sun and air, water and soil,
plants need all four to grow
when we are tiny, we need care
when grown up, we are good to go!

'You have been very kind;
you are caring and gentle, too
you helped me and many more trees
like you always do.'

'Thank you so much!' the sapling said
as the clouds gave a smile
'It's always a pleasure to help others!'
And, whoosh! They went towards
the next dry mile.

Art in the Sky

Many countless stars
were all dressed and ready
to shine like gems at night,
holding their places steady.

Tiny, the little star,
was feeling quite low
its smile was lost
and so was its radiant glow.

Wise, the big star nearby,
saw Tiny alone and sad,
'What is it,' Wise asked,
'that is making you feel so bad?

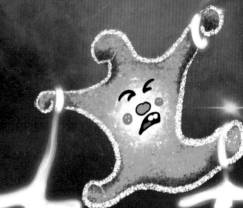

'I feel like I am stuck!
in the same place forever.
I want to see new things!
Will that happen ever?'

'Oh! Is that why you are sad?
then you need to know:
we are presently enrolling
for the sky's grand nightly show.

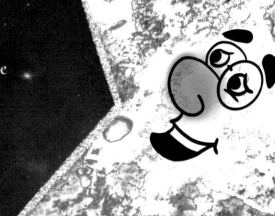

'You see, in the sky each night,
constellations make many a shape
coming up next is a superhero
donning a dress and a cape!

'If you wish, and if you choose,
you too can have a role
we do have some missing spots
if you want a part of the whole.'

'Oh, yes, oh, yes!'
replied a smiling Tiny,
'what do I have to do?
would you tell me,
please do, please do!'

Wise then spilled the super-secret,
'You, is what you have to be,
and all you have to do is
focus your eyes, and see!'

Tiny, for the first time then,
saw the magic unfold
as it opened its eyes wide
to see what cannot be told.

Magical lines ran across the sky
like waves dancing in an ocean!
It could see the superhero
almost real, almost in motion.

'Wow!' thought Tiny, the star,
'why did I never see this before?
there is so much yet to see,
so many shapes to explore!'

The little star was sad no more
and was happy as it could be,
'Thank you, O dear Wise!
Thank you for helping me see.'

And to this day Tiny the star
makes something new each night;
if you look up closely, and see,
you'll find those shapes shining bright.

Nature's
Melody

Melody the nightingale
sang to herself a sweet solo song
I wonder what it'd be like, she thought,
if there was someone to sing along.

It is such a pleasant day to sing:
Chirp tweet chirp, tweet tweet
if only I could find a partner
it would be so nice and sweet.

Let me fly and find someone
who would like to sing with me
she flew and flew, but alas!
all birds she met were very busy!

Tired, she sat, and tried to sing.
Her notes were now off beat;
I cannot sing like this, she thought,
that's no rhythm for dancing feet

She flew again, this time, very far
until she came to a forest small.
She perched on a branch to rest
and, then, she started to hear it all.

The water swayed in the stream nearby:
Swish splash, swoosh swoosh
the wind whispered through the leaves:
whiff whizz, whoosh whoosh

A busy bee, in search of nectar,
went buzz buzz, buzz buzz
the hummingbird flapped nearby:
Humm humm humm humm

Voices of the forest, she thought
Oh! These are wonderful!
Maybe I can sing with nature
and my song could be beautiful!

Her heart was now fresh and rested
her music had found a new beat
she sang in sync with nature
a tune for every dancing feet.

Water and wind, buzzes and hums
all had a part to play
the song sung in rhythm with nature
made Melody smile and sway.

I wonder why I was lost
when nature was always around me
all I had to do was listen closely
and open my eyes to see.

Nature is the best companion
and what an inspiration it can be
when I opened my eyes and ears
I found a music partner for me.

Fun with Mr. Sun

Hello there, Mr. Sun!
How do you do today?
If I asked you a few questions
I wonder what you would say.

Do you ever feel the heat?
Does it become too hot to bear?
I wonder what you do for fun,
would you like to share?

Would you like to swim in the sea?
Or ski down a snowy slope?
Or feel the chilling wind in your fac
when zip-lining down a long rope?

Would you like a pair of shades?
It would help with the glare, I thin
how about some refreshing juice?
or maybe an iced lemon drink?

Would you like a giant umbrella
and relax under it, on a pool chair?
Taking a break from the heat,
I have sun screen that I can share!

Would you like the clouds
to hose you with some rain?
You must feel so very hot
but you never complain!

Would you like to sit under a shady tree
to eat a delicious snack?
Some ice, some fruits, some treats
in a picnic bag, for you I can pack.

Would you like a fan to cool you off,
running at full speed?
How about some soothing music?
Or a funny story to read?

Would you like to go on a drive
to places near and far?
Or deep in the galaxy,
in a fast convertible car?

Would you like to play board games
Oh, those are a lot of fun!
Or watch your favourite movie
while eating buttery popcorn?

I wonder all the time
what you would like to do,
although I may never know
I have to say this to you:

Thank you for the gift of life!
For all the warmth and light,
for shining every day for us,
for making our days so bright!

Rain Dance

The clouds roared loud and clear
and lights flashed up high
there was a light and sound show
on what was a calm, blue sky.

The clouds were in their full glory
doing what they enjoyed the most
pouring down rain on everyone,
like a gigantic water hose.

And what a show it turned out to be!
Everyone stopped to see
one by one, and quickly
nature and people joined the party.

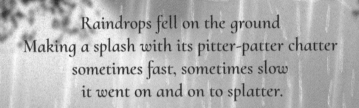

Raindrops fell on the ground
Making a splash with its pitter-patter chatter
sometimes fast, sometimes slow
it went on and on to splatter.

The peacock spread its wings to show the beautiful colors
it looked like a giant umbrella that danced with full vigor.

The trees got a full shower
washing away the dirt so brown,
now adorning a fresh new green
everything was fresh around.

Leaves swayed with wind and rain
dancing to their own beat
children ran out of homes
as fast as they could with their happy feet.

Frogs and toads croaked and hopped
enjoying the refreshing rain
everyone danced, everyone jumped
everyone splashed again and again!

From a seat high up in the sky
the sun watched all the glee
then, it knocked on the clouds, and said,
'Please open the door, it's time for me.'

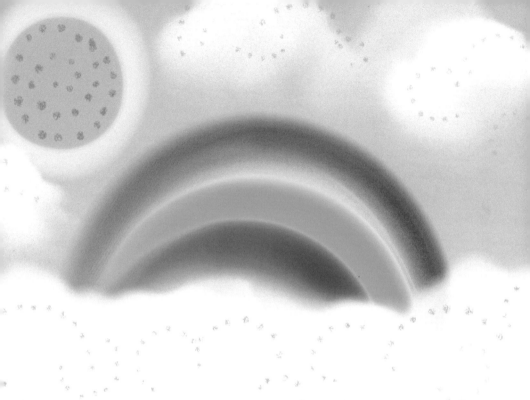

The clouds parted for the sun to shine;
its rays cut through the water and air;
light bent as if almost by magic
and a rainbow appeared in all its flair!

The sun danced and brought to the party
a bridge of seven colors in the sky;
what a gorgeous, beautiful, colorful rainbow!
until it was time to say goodbye.

The clouds moved on, and so did the rain
the sun shone bright once again
Oh! What fun it was for all!
To jump and dance in the rain.

Buzzy,
the Busy Bee

Buzz buzz buzz buzz buzz
the workday had just begun
Buzzy, the hardworking, busy bee
had a list of things to be done.

A purple pansy that it first went to
got tickled by the bee
it moved and swayed so much
that Buzzy had to flee.

Giggles, hee and haa!
went on for a while
Buzzy and Purple had so much fun
they couldn't help laugh and smile

It flew to a pink tulip next;
when a very strong breeze
pushed the bee away and
made the tulip sneeze.

Everything seemed to pause,
And then, Aa, aaa aaaa achoooooooooo!
'Excuse me,' said the tulip and sniffled
Buzzy said, 'Oh, dear! Bless you!'

He saw a dash of red at a distance
and went for a closer look
but it was no sweet, fragrant rose,
it turned out to be a book.

achoooooooooooo!

The orange poppy it saw farther away
was not in full bloom even today
I'll have to wait, thought Buzzy
I'll come back to you another day.

The bluebonnet had a fresh fragrance
but it was busy a whole lot
there were so many other bugs there
Buzzy couldn't find a spot.

Then there was a violet lavender
that wanted to help the bee
but all the buzzing sound
made the flower dizzy.

Buzzy buzzed on and on
making friends with all he met
then he heard a faint whisper
Buzzy wondered, what was that?